BURN AFTER WRITING

A catalogue record for this book is available from the British Library.
Second edition 2016.
First published in Great Britain in 2014 by Carpet Bombing Culture.
An imprint of Pro-actif Communications.

www.carpetbombingculture.co.uk
email: books@carpetbombingculture.co.uk

ISBN: 978-1-908211-23-1

BURN AFTER WRITING

The Pen is Mightier than the Keyboard

Handwriting, like a fingerprint, like a singing voice, like a footstep - each one is unique. Each one betrays as much in itself as in the intention with which it is used. You give yourself away when you take pen to paper.

In the age of infinite and instant reproduction only the unique is still beautiful. Will your descendants ever read your Facebook Timeline?

Save something for the real world, which remains, after all, the only place where we can really be ourselves. Write something beautiful by hand and you can be sure it will last for eternity.

IN A NUTSHELL

Welcome to an opportunity to face lifes big questions.

Who are you now? How did you get here? Where are you going?

Burn After Writing offers probing questions, mind games, thought experiments and homework assignments all on your favourite subject - yourself.

Have fun with it, or take it too seriously, or both. It's up to you.

But when you finish with it make sure you bury it, hide it, lock it up and run away. . . or Burn After Writing.

In a society where where we 'share' our everything, BAW goes against the grain and politely asks you to 'share' nothing

WELCOME TO THE BOOK OF YOU

This is your Black Dossier. Hidden in the secret compartment of your world. For your eyes only. The place where you speak your own truth freely, beyond any concern for how it might be viewed by others. The only space in your life where you can take off all the masks.

It's an extended feature length interview with you, a radical thought experiment with you as the subject and you as the result.

As adults we learn to focus on representing ourselves in a manner pleasing others. Why don't you leave that behind you for a minute. Take some time out, grab a coffee and indulge yourself with Burn After Writing by lamplight.

Some elements are random like tea leaves forming patterns in a mug, some elements are more deliberate, to coax you into realising things about yourself you never noticed before.

It's time to play a game of Truth or Dare with yourself. How honest can you really be with only you watching?

DISCLAIMER

If you are not you then you may not go further. For it is not written. You cannot simply skip in here without a care in the world and start prancing about the pages willy nilly. No. You must be initiated into the cult of B.A.W.

Before you go on, like the fool about to step off a cliff, stop here a moment and consider the sacred values of the cult of B.A.W.

- I WILL ANSWER WITH RELENTLESS, PAINFULLY SEARCHING HONESTY ALL QUESTIONS WITHIN.

- I WILL USE THE POWER OF THE MAGICAL RANDOM 'AVAFLICKTHRU' TO SELECT THE MOST RELEVANT QUESTION FOR MY PRESENT STATE .

- I WILL TAKE A WALK THROUGH THE CORRIDORS OF MY MIND AND OPEN ALL LOCKED DOORS.

If you can commit to these noble and courageous values then by all means you are welcome to join the society of truth and self knowledge. Copy out the following statement in your own handwriting:

I pledge my allegiance to the cult of B.A.W.

Now you may proceed. Keep the faith. And select a page at random. (Or is it selecting you . . ?)

BURN AFTER WRITING

THE TRUTH

You can't hide from the truth but it sure as damn can hide from you

They say the artist is one who uses lies to tell the truth. One thing's for sure, it's impossible to tell the whole truth, especially when you are writing about you.

Sometimes the lie is in the omission. Sometimes the lie is in spin. But there is always an element of fiction, because the talking or the writing is not the thing itself, the gap between the word and the moment is always too wide.

How honest can you be with these questions? How does it feel to tell the truth?

I suppose the real question here is this, how possible is it to see yourself clearly through your own supremely biased eyes?

However you choose to use this book, think about 'the truth' before you answer.

At least then you might know if you're lying or not.

*You can't look at something without changing it,
you can't look at yourself without changing.*

THE PAST

THE PAST

Maybe you can't change what actually happened, but the way you remember it is never the same twice. Every time we remember something, we relive it from a different camera angle.

We always reinvent our history to suit the present need. Tonight let's do the opposite. Try and find new storylines in the fragments of your own history, storylines that completely recreate your relationship to the present. It's a fun game with no rules - but there are lots of rules. Only you know what they are. Proceed.

My earliest memory

As a child, I dreamt of becoming

When I look into the past, the thing I miss the most

LOOKING BACK

The music I loved as a child

The first thing I bought with my own money

The age at which I became an adult

The person who had the greatest impact on my life

The person I have loved the most

The hardest thing I've ever done

If I could do it all over again, I would change

The first song I ever remember hearing

Things I collected as a child

My aspirations as a child

The teacher that had the most influence on my life

My parents were . . .

My first pet

My best friend growing up

The long lost childhood possession that I would love to see again

The one thing I regret in the whole world

Things that I have been addicted to

I was most happiest when

The book that has had the greatest influence on my life

The craziest thing I have ever done in my life

The most dramatic fork in the road, in my life

3 things I am glad I tried but will never do again . . .

1: _____

2: _____

3: _____

I will never forgive

The 5 best times I've ever had in my life

1: _____

2: _____

3: _____

4: _____

5: _____

5 things that I have always wanted to do but have never done.

1: _____

2: _____

3: _____

4: _____

5: _____

The last time I said 'I love you'

People I miss

My greatest heartbreak

The smartest choice I made as a teenager

I feel guilty for

I wish I had never met

My life story in 3 sentences

Baggage I am carrying

A FEW OF MY FAVOURITE THINGS

Every now and then something comes along that knocks you off your feet. You feel like you have finally been understood, like somebody looked into your soul and wrote a song just for you. And as you grow, they grow with you, making your life richer.

A FEW OF MY FAVOURITE THINGS

THE TOP 5 (OF ALL TIME)

TOP 5 BANDS

1: _____

2: _____

3: _____

4: _____

5: _____

TOP 5 ALBUMS

1: _____

2: _____

3: _____

4: _____

5: _____

TOP 5 SONGS

1: _____

2: _____

3: _____

4: _____

5: _____

THE TOP 5 (OF ALL TIME)

TOP 5 GIGS/CONCERTS

1: _____

2: _____

3: _____

4: _____

5: _____

TOP 5 BOOKS

1: _____

2: _____

3: _____

4: _____

5: _____

TOP 5 MOVIES

1: _____

2: _____

3: _____

4: _____

5: _____

THE TOP 5 (OF ALL TIME)

TOP 5 PLACES IN THE WORLD

1: _____

2: _____

3: _____

4: _____

5: _____

TOP 5 CITIES

1: _____

2: _____

3: _____

4: _____

5: _____

TOP 5 MOST AMAZING EXPERIENCES

1: _____

2: _____

3: _____

4: _____

5: _____

THE TOP 5 (OF ALL TIME)

TOP 5 "REGULAR" PEOPLE

1: _____

2: _____

3: _____

4: _____

5: _____

TOP 5 CELEBRITIES

1: _____

2: _____

3: _____

4: _____

5: _____

TOP 5 CREATIVE GENIUSES

1: _____

2: _____

3: _____

4: _____

5: _____

If I could spend 48 hours with anyone (living or dead), it would it be

How cool would my 16-year-old self think I am right now

If I could have lived through any time period, it would have been

The last 3 years of my life described in 3 words:

1: _____

2: _____

3: _____

The 3 things have I accomplished in the last 12 months that I am most proud of:

1: _____

2: _____

3: _____

The most defining moment of my life so far

I'm haunted by

5 milestone experiences that made me the person that I am today

1: _____

2: _____

3: _____

4: _____

5: _____

My favourite childhood memory

The hardest choice I have ever had to make

The stupidest thing I have ever done

QUICK FIRE

I've

Been in love ( ) Failed my driving test ( )

Jumped out of a plane ( ) Broken a bone ( ) Won a trophy ( )

Learned another language ( ) Been to a Spa ( )

Kissed someone and regretted it ( ) Smoked a cigar ( )

Rode in an ambulance ( ) Turned someone down ( )

Flown in a helicopter ( ) Met someone famous ( )

Written my will ( ) Read my partners internet history ( )

Know the words to the national anthem ( )

Been a godparent ( ) Buried someone ( ) Got married ( )

Showered with someone else ( ) Given blood ( )

Memorised a poem ( ) Broken something expensive ( )

Considered cosmetic surgery ( ) Bungee jumped ( )

Had Cosmetic Surgery ( ) Danced with my mother/father ( )

Jumped off the high board ( ) Dived off the high board ( )

Been on a diet ( ) Had an invisible friend ( )

Been a best man/bridesmaid ( ) Dated someone twice ( )

Won a competition ( ) Deleted my internet history ( )

Made a speech in front of an audience ( )

QUICK FIRE

I've

Stayed out all night ( ) Been on a blind date ( )

Had a massage ( ) Sung karaoke ( ) Watched the sun rise ( )

Watched the sun set ( ) Lost at a Casino ( ) Faked it ( )

Grown my own food ( ) Changed a car tyre ( ) Kissed a stranger ( )

Been on TV ( ) Given money to a street beggar ( ) Got divorced ( )

Handwritten a love letter ( ) Climbed a mountain ( )

Had a crush on someone of the same sex ( ) Been on a diet twice ( )

Sent a message in a bottle ( ) Know at least one good joke ( )

Worked for minimum wage ( ) Cheated on someone ( )

Won a bet ( ) Written poetry ( ) Performed on stage ( )

Fired a gun ( ) Been to a school reunion ( ) DJ'd ( )

Ridden a mechanical bull ( ) Learned first aid ( )

Saved someones life ( ) Broken someones heart ( )

Voluteered for Charity ( ) Lied to a Police Officer ( )

Learnt a card trick ( ) Got a degree ( ) Had a penpal ( )

Stayed up for 24 hours straight ( ) Sponsored a child ( )

Done the splits ( ) Lied to the doctor ( ) Got Married Again ( )

Signed up as an organ donor ( ) Had a Tarot Card reading ( )

THINGS THAT I HAVE
LEARNED ALONG THE WAY...

THINGS THAT I HAVE
LEARNED ALONG THE WAY...

I CONFESS

Nothing lightens the soul quite like a good hearty confession. Let these pages act as your confessional box.

I CONFESS

YOLO
You`Only Live Once

THE PRESENT

THE PRESENT

This is the same moment in which all of history occurred. Everything is contained in it. Nothing lies without.

Everybody wants you to live for the moment. Primarily because it is easier to sell things to a goldfish with ADHD. But where are you actually right now? To answer that you have to step outside the present moment into a space of reflection.

You have to stop time, get off the ride and look back on it. The only way to really see the present is to be outside of it. So put yourself into words. Freeze your restless subjectivity into a crystallised state, like crushing a butterfly inside a scrapbook.

See through the chaotic circus of the lived moment to the gems of relevant truth beyond.

Where are you at? Right now?
Who are you right now?

The biggest inspiration in my life

My most prized possession

Today I learnt

Things I should let go of

If I was given £5000, I would spend it on

The one song that makes the hairs on the back of my neck stand up

The one thing I want to change about myself

3 things that are getting on my nerves right now

The first 5 songs that play when I press shuffle on my Media Player

1: _____

2: _____

3: _____

4: _____

5: _____

If I could have a conversation today with one person from history, it would be

My life quote

The one relationship I would like to fix

Things that make me happy

If a genie granted me 3 wishes, they would be

1: _____

2: _____

3: _____

My autobiography would be called

My favourite 'little things' in life

If I could give one thing to one person it would be

Things that make me laugh

I secretly envy

If I could be anywhere in the world right now

If I could be a fly on the wall . . .

My greatest fear

THIS IS WHO I AM

Live for the now or plan for the future?
Everybody seems to have their own idea.

Listen. Don't listen. Be where you are. Be who you are.

Everybody tells you these are the best days of your life.
So much pressure! They're all wrong. Be where you are.
Nobody else is really having any more fun than you are,
they're all just pretending.

THIS IS WHO I AM

The thing that I am working on that is BIG

My personality in 6 words

1: _____   4: _____

2: _____   5: _____

3: _____   6: _____

If I didn't know how old I was, I would think I was

If I could choose to stay a certain age forever, it would be

If I could go to the fridge right now and find one thing

5 things I need in my life

1: _____

2: _____

3: _____

4: _____

5: _____

5 things I want in my life

1: _____

2: _____

3: _____

4: _____

5: _____

LET'S BE HONEST...

Let's be honest.
Let's pretend there is something under the mask.
Is there? Who are you?

I am: _____

I'm not: _____

I adore: _____

I detest: _____

I have: _____

I have never: _____

I like: _____

I don't like: _____

I love: _____

I hate: _____

LET'S BE HONEST...

I need: _____

I want: _____

I can: _____

I can't: _____

I'm always: _____

I'm never: _____

I'm afraid of: _____

I'm not afraid to: _____

I'm pretty good at: _____

I'm rubbish at: _____

I want more: _____

I want less: _____

I can never respect...

If I could change my first name, I would change it to

If I had to be trapped in a TV show, it would be

If I could lock one person in a room and torment them for a day, that person would be

The one thing I don't mind spending proper money on

If I had a brainwashing machine, I would use it on

The first song to come into my head right now is

If I was to win the lottery, this amount would be enough

If I could pick up the phone right now and call one person, living or dead, it would be

I AM

Circle one of the two characteristics on each line that you feel best describes your personality.

Anxious OR Calm

Stubborn OR Flexible

Daring OR Cautious

Moody OR Cheerful

See Big Picture OR Detail-orientated

Competitive OR Cooperative

Pessimistic OR Optimistic

Patient OR Hasty

Suspicious OR Trusting

THE LAST WORD

Fleeting moments fly past us whistling in the wind. Can you catch one out of the air like Mr Miyagi catching flies with chopsticks in the original Karate Kid (not the remake)?

Last film: _____

Last book: _____

Last gig: _____

Last time I cried: _____

Last song I listened to: _____

Last time I was scared: _____

Last time I danced: _____

Last time I was angry: _____

Last time I laughed: _____

Last time I was drunk: _____

I need to forgive

If I could clean up one mess, it would be

The one skill I wish I could possess

If I was exiled to a foreign land for the rest of my life, I would like it to be

My foolproof recipe for mending a broken heart

The 3 finest meals I have ever produced by my own hand

1: _____

2: _____

3: _____

If I had to sacrifice one of my relatives to save the world, it would be

If my house was on fire, the 3 things I would grab are

1: _____

2: _____

3: _____

ONE WORD...

Think fast. Better still don't think at all. Sidestep your own mental filters and cut to the chase. Don't pause, don't ponder and don't criticise. If you could say everything you wanted with just one word...

My job: _____

My partner: _____

My body: _____

My love life: _____

My sanctuary: _____

My fear: _____

My childhood: _____

My addiction: _____

My passion: _____

My kryptonite: _____

My regret: _____

ONE WORD...

My turn on: _____

My turn off: _____

My hero: _____

My future: _____

My fantasy: _____

My achilles heel: _____

My guilt: _____

My greatest virtue: _____

My vice: _____

The outcome is bigger than the sum of its parts:

_____+_____+_____ = *Family*

_____+_____+_____ = *Love*

_____+_____+_____ = *Life*

Looking at the lives of my friends, this is who I think has got it right

If I could install 3 complete languages in my brain (with zero effort), I would choose

If I could bring one person back from the dead right now it would be

The single biggest waste of energy in my life right now

People I'd like to punch in the face

If I could go back in time and witness any historical event, it would be

The things that are taboo for me, the things I find hard to talk about even with close friends

People to be forgiven

PEOPLE THAT MEAN
SOMETHING TO ME

PLACES THAT MEAN SOMETHING TO ME

The things I find ridiculous

If I could make one thing vanish forever, it would be

My parents in 5 words

1: _____

2: _____

3: _____

4: _____

5: _____

The biggest hole in my life was left by

If I was given £10,000 today on the condition that I couldn't keep the money for myself, I would . . .

Right now, at this moment, the thing I want the most is

The one word I would use to describe the relationship with my mother

The one word I would use to describe the relationship with my father

If I could direct the Hollywood movie of my life story it would be called:

and this would be the cast list

_____ AS me _____

_____ AS _____

_____ AS _____

_____ AS _____

_____ AS _____

_____ AS _____

The song for the opening credits of the movie of my life

The song for the main theme of the movie of my life

The song for the closing titles of the movie of my life

Religion in 3 words

1: _____   *2:* _____   *3:* _____

If I had to sing one karaoke tune in a crowded bar of strangers, my song would be

If I were to host a dinner party and I could invite three people (dead or alive) as fellow diners, they would be

The full names of my children today (born or otherwise)

One word to describe my current love life

SOMETHING THAT
MEANS SOMETHING

MY ATTRIBUTES

Be honest. You judge everybody you meet. We all do.
How about judging yourself for a change?

Honesty	1	2	3	4	5	6	7	8	9	10
Generosity	1	2	3	4	5	6	7	8	9	10
Forgiveness	1	2	3	4	5	6	7	8	9	10
Happiness	1	2	3	4	5	6	7	8	9	10
Loyalty	1	2	3	4	5	6	7	8	9	10
Uniqueness	1	2	3	4	5	6	7	8	9	10
Humour	1	2	3	4	5	6	7	8	9	10
Intelligence	1	2	3	4	5	6	7	8	9	10
Accommodating	1	2	3	4	5	6	7	8	9	10
Talented	1	2	3	4	5	6	7	8	9	10
Confidence	1	2	3	4	5	6	7	8	9	10
Humbleness	1	2	3	4	5	6	7	8	9	10
Loving	1	2	3	4	5	6	7	8	9	10
Tolerance	1	2	3	4	5	6	7	8	9	10
Spontaneity	1	2	3	4	5	6	7	8	9	10
Health	1	2	3	4	5	6	7	8	9	10
Creativity	1	2	3	4	5	6	7	8	9	10
Fashionable	1	2	3	4	5	6	7	8	9	10

I am sick to death of hearing about

If no one was watching I would

The most valuable thing I own is

My guiltiest pleasure

If I could make one thing disappear today, it would be

My secret skill

The song title that best describes my life

If I had two weeks to live, I would

The one thing that I do that I would like to be able to stop

If I could change one current event in the world it would be

I'm worried about

WORD ASSOCIATION

When I say 'life', you say what? Don't think; just write the first word that comes into your head. Let your subconscious mind do the talking. You might be surprised at what you discover about yourself through the magical power of randomicity.

WORD ASSOCIATION

Life: _____   Religion: _____

Work: _____   Domination: _____

Trust: _____   Love: _____

Fame: _____   Family: _____

Forgiveness: _____   Sacrifice: _____

Weakness: _____   Age: _____

Death: _____   Honesty: _____

Discipline: _____   War: _____

Lies: _____   Success: _____

Sadness: _____   Lust: _____

Past: _____   Fear: _____

Sex: _____   Home: _____

Excess: _____   Drugs: _____

Hate: _____   Future: _____

Innocence: _____   Failure: _____

Victim: _____   Destiny: _____

Violence: _____   Humour: _____

Regret: _____   Envy: _____

Mother: _____   Honesty: _____

5 things I love to hate

1: _____

2: _____

3: _____

4: _____

5: _____

The nicest thing I've ever done that no one knows about?

At the end of the day, who will be there for me

On a scale of 1 to 10, how happy am I with my life?

1   2   3   4   5   6   7   8   9   10

What would make it a 10?

My darkest secret

MY LIFE IN TRIVIA

Birthplace: _____

Siblings: _____

Currently residing: _____

Social class: _____

Occupation: _____

Zodiac sign: _____

Political party: _____

Allergy: _____

Pet: _____

Charity: _____

Newspaper: _____

Magazine: _____

Drink: _____

Breakfast: _____

Starter: _____

Main course: _____

Dessert: _____

Restaurant: _____

Bar: _____

MY LIFE IN TRIVIA

Club: _____

Hotel: _____

Clothing: _____

Shoes: _____

Car: _____

Phone: _____

Camera: _____

Dream job: _____

Subscription: _____

Computer: _____

Brand: _____

Shop: _____

Comfort food: _____

Hobby: _____

Pastime: _____

Team: _____

Game: _____

Website: _____

TV programme: _____

FAMILY IS

FAMILY IS

The advice that has shaped me the most

How in control of my life do I feel right now

1   2   3   4   5   6   7   8   9   10

What would make it a 10?

My dream job

My favourite food

My most treasured possession

My perfect Saturday night

Something I've wished for repeatedly

My hidden talent

The things that I am really bad at

The one movie that I could watch over and over again

ALL TIME FAVOURITES

Song: _____

Album: _____

Gig: _____

Place: _____

Movie: _____

Book: _____

Band: _____

Artist: _____

Holiday: _____

City: _____

Teacher: _____

Word: _____

TV Programme: _____

PRICELESS

The things that money can't buy...

WALK ON THE WILD SIDE

Sometimes the right thing to do is the wrong thing.
Sensible people are basically idiots. We're not sure how
that adds up but it does. The world is wrong, so how can
doing wrong in the eyes of the world possibly be wrong?

Things I've done:

☐ Been Skinny Dipping

☐ Been in a police car

☐ Taken drugs

☐ Been drunk

☐ Been in a fight

☐ Seen someone/thing die

☐ Partied all night

☐ Smoked cigarettes

☐ Been fired from a job

☐ Had stitches

☐ Had a tattoo

☐ Faked it

☐ Crashed a party

☐ Cheated on a test

☐ Danced in the moonlight

☐ Skipped a class

☐ Stolen something

☐ Been to a music festival

☐ Joined the mile high club

☐ Kissed someone of the same sex

WALK ON THE WILD SIDE

- ☐ Got a piercing
- ☐ Dyed my hair
- ☐ Kissed a stranger
- ☐ Had a friend with benefits
- ☐ Had my heart broken
- ☐ Gone commando
- ☐ Eaten something that's alive
- ☐ Had sex outdoors
- ☐ Had cosmetic surgery
- ☐ Been thrown out of a club
- ☐ Protested against something
- ☐ Cheated on someone
- ☐ Fired a gun
- ☐ Taken revenge
- ☐ Smoked a cigar
- ☐ Broken the speed limit
- ☐ Drank champagne straight out of the bottle
- ☐ Played cards for money
- ☐ Fallen in love with someone I shouldn't have
- ☐ Bought Porn
- ☐ Cross dressed
- ☐ Been to a strip club
- ☐ Shoplifted
- ☐ Prank Called Someone
- ☐ Skipped Work
- ☐ Killed an Animal

Where am I going?

THE FUTURE

THE FUTURE

Predicting your future requires an element of self-delusion. The difficulty is that sometimes we can make something happen as we intend to and sometimes we cannot. And even when the intention is clear, the consequences must always be largely unforeseen. Fortunately our intention is rarely very clear.

Where are you going? Where are you going? Where are you going? But really, where are you going though? How about now? And now? And be clear on this, the question is not where do you want to go or even where do you fancifully dream you will end up. Look at what you actually do. Look at the patterns in the rhythm of your everyday life and extrapolate accordingly. Remember to take this section very seriously because then it will be much funnier when you come to read it in ten years time.

And with our course set for the straits of foolhardy prediction, let us begin...

My future in 3 words

1: _____

2: _____

3: _____

The one thing I'm most excited about

The one thing I'm most concerned about

My ideal home

The risk I would take if I knew I could not fail

The one thing that I would be prepared to die for

3 things I need to let go of

1: _____

2: _____

3: _____

? OR ?

This beats the Myers Briggs personality profiling matrix any day of the week. Remember - it's not what you're like that counts in this shallow world...it's what you like

The Ride	OR	The Destination
The Stones	OR	The Beatles
Mac	OR	PC
Wine	OR	Spirits
Rich	OR	Famous
BMW	OR	Mercedes
Sweet	OR	Salted
Meat	OR	Murder
God	OR	The Big Bang
Pepsi	OR	Coke
London	OR	New York
Nike	OR	Adidas
Tea	OR	Coffee
Gay	OR	Straight
Movies	OR	Music
Summer	OR	Winter
Political Left	OR	Right
Truth	OR	Dare
Spirituality	OR	Religion
Climate Change Fact	OR	Fiction
City	OR	Country
Death Penalty	OR	Life Imprisonment
Hitchcock	OR	Spielberg
See The Future	OR	Change The Past
Las Vegas	OR	Paris

? OR ?

Art	OR	Science
Fame	OR	Money
Brains	OR	Beauty
Going Out	OR	Staying In
iPhone	OR	Samsung
More Time	OR	More Money
Subway	OR	McDonalds
Watch The Movie	OR	Read The Book
Lennon	OR	McCartney
Freedom	OR	Security
Mountains	OR	Beach
Creativity	OR	Knowledge
Tattoos	OR	Piercings
The Wire	OR	The Sopranos
Money	OR	Looks
Odd	OR	Even
Appetizer	OR	Dessert
Adventure	OR	Relaxation
Telephone	OR	Text
Celebrity	OR	Artist
Cremation	OR	Burial
Winning Is Everything	OR	It's Taking Part That Matters
How Things Work	OR	How Things Look
Form	OR	Functionality
Thoughts	OR	Emotions
Slow	OR	Fast
Optimist	OR	Pessimist
Realist	OR	Idealist
Head	OR	Heart

.... or neither

Something I think that everyone should experience in their lifetime

The greatest enemy of the future of mankind

My dream reunion

If I could go on a gap year right now it would be to

The victory am I working towards

.

My next challenge

The 3 things that I have been putting off that I need to do

The one thing I'll do with my children differently to what my parents did with me

The biggest challenge facing the world today

THE FUTURE IS

Let's play the predictions game!
What do you want from the future?

THE FUTURE IS

My bucket list of 10 places to go before I die

1: _____

2: _____

3: _____

4: _____

5: _____

6: _____

7: _____

8: _____

9: _____

10: _____

Books I want to read

1: _____

2: _____

3: _____

4: _____

5: _____

6: _____

7: _____

8: _____

9: _____

10: _____

MY FAVOURITE LYRICS/POETRY

MY FAVOURITE LYRICS/POETRY

In ten years time my money is coming from

I would like to retire to

My perfect road trip

I must make room for

I dream of

The things that scare me about getting old

If I could spend my last hours of life with anyone, doing anything, I would

If I could be laid to rest anywhere, I would like it to be

The one song that I would like to be played at my funeral

My legacy is

PLAYLIST

These songs are the soundtrack to my life

1: _____

2: _____

3: _____

4: _____

5: _____

6: _____

7: _____

8: _____

9: _____

10: _____

VOW – NOW

Circle your pledges. Add your own!

Say no

Forgive myself for my mistakes

Have no regrets

Prioritise

Sleep more

Treat myself

Shake things up

Give more

Fall in love

Take responsibility

Accept criticism

Make art

Be Me

Work smarter not harder

Worry less

Help others

VOW – NOW

Embrace change

Love more

Listen more

Don't hate

Take chances

Tell the truth

Be assertive

Be more humble

Relax more

Apologise

Lighten up

Eat good food

Smile more

Travel More

Dream big

Feel good anyway

Give credit, take blame

Be thankful

THE FUTURE STARTS HERE

In one week from now I will:

In one month from now I will:

In 1 year from now I will:

In 10 years from now I will:

MY LIFE RULES

#1 _____

_____

#2 _____

_____

#3 _____

_____

#4 _____

_____

#5 _____

_____

THE BUCKET LIST

Nothing lasts forever, least of all you. Let a little contemplation on mortality rev up your engines and reboot your lust for life. Old death maybe coming on his bony horse, but you won't go softly into that goodnight. Give yourself something good to flash before your eyes in the ultimate moment.

Cross things off this list and then start your own:

Be happy
Run half marathon
Do a triathlon
Ski/snowboard
Canoe
Ride a horse
Learn a language
Play a musical instrument
Sing in a choir
Dance Salsa
Ride in a hot air balloon
Jump out of a plane
Scuba Dive
White Water Raft
Play chess
Make Pottery
Paint a picture
Write a short story
Solve Rubiks Cube
Volunteer/fundraise
Start my own business
Ride a motorbike
Write a book
Donate blood
Bungee Jump

Go camping
Climb a mountain
Plant a tree
Fly in a helicopter
Fire a gun
Go backpacking
Give to charity
Go rock climbing
Learn to juggle
Write my will
Milk a cow
Be part of a flash mob
Learn a martial art
Learn first aid
Learn to fly
Get a tattoo
Start a blog
Join a gym
Bake a cake
Find my 'thing'
Learn to meditate
Go on a road trip
Try yoga
Learn to knit
Be happy

MY BUCKET LIST

10 things to do before I die

1: _____

2: _____

3: _____

4: _____

5: _____

6: _____

7: _____

8: _____

9: _____

10: _____

I WANT LESS

I WANT MORE

LIFE IS

Freedom is being able to make your own definitions.

Life is: _____

Regret is: _____

Success is: _____

Children are: _____

Death is: _____

Happiness is: _____

LIFE IS

Love is: _____

Faith is: _____

Work is: _____

Money is: _____

Peace is: _____

Religion is: _____

Politics is: _____

STUFF I WANT TO PASS ON

Imagine you have nine minutes to live and you have a pen and paper. You can get a message to your children or someone close giving them the best that you have learned. Give them something to carry with them in their own lives. What do you have to pass on? Go!

STUFF I WANT TO PASS ON

LOVE IS

LOVE IS

MY INSPIRATION

You inspire me. The thing that makes me hungry for more life. Longing to grow in the direction that you have shown to me is possible. Not to follow you of course but to seek what you sought.

MY INSPIRATION

MY PARTNER

The future is: _____

Our special moment: _____

Our song: _____

Our city: _____

5 THINGS I LOVE ABOUT YOU

1: _____

2: _____

3: _____

4: _____

5: _____

MY PARTNER

My turns ons: _____

My turn offs: _____

1 thing I'd change about you: _____

My confession: _____

5 THINGS YOU DO THAT DRIVE ME CRAZY

1: _____

2: _____

3: _____

4: _____

5: _____

MY PARTNER

My Perfect date night

Where it all started

What I love about you

I'll love you more if ...

THEY ARE

Circle one of the two characteristics on each line that you feel best describes your partners personality.

Anxious OR *Calm*

Stubborn OR *Flexible*

Daring OR *Cautious*

Moody OR *Cheerful*

See Big Picture OR *Detail-orientated*

Competitive OR *Cooperative*

Pessimistic OR *Optimistic*

Patient OR *Hasty*

Suspicious OR *Trusting*

A LETTER TO MY FUTURE SELF

A LETTER TO MY FUTURE SELF